Tadpoles

Ashok's Dog

by Pippa Goodhart

Illustrated by Mike Phillips

FRANKLIN WATTS

LONDON • SYDNEY

Pippa Goodhart

"At a dog rescue home a scruffy, hairy puppy knocked my mum over into some nettles. We chose that puppy and called him 'Rags'. He was lovely."

Mike Phillips

"I love drawing animals, especially dogs. I drew a picture of Poppy, my own dog, for this story. See if you can guess which one she is – she loves chasing her tail!"

"I want a dog," said Ashok.

"What kind of dog?"
asked Dad.

"I think I want a big dog," said Ashok.

"Or maybe not," said Dad.

8

"I think I want a fast dog," said Ashok.

"Or maybe not,"
said Dad.

12

13

Ashok saw dogs that were sweet ...

funny ...

14

smart ...

and scruffy.

"I don't know which dog to choose!" said Ashok.

"Then let the dog choose you," said Dad.

19

All the dogs ran
past Ashok ...

except one.

"This is the dog
for me!" said Ashok.

Notes for adults

TADPOLES are structured to provide support for newly independent readers. The stories may also be used by adults for sharing with young children.

Starting to read alone can be daunting. **TADPOLES** help by providing visual support and repeating words and phrases. These books will both develop confidence and encourage reading and rereading for pleasure.

If you are reading this book with a child, here are a few suggestions:

1. Make reading fun! Choose a time to read when you and the child are relaxed and have time to share the story.
2. Talk about the story before you start reading. Look at the cover and the blurb. What might the story be about? Why might the child like it?
3. Encourage the child to reread the story, and to retell the story in their own words, using the illustrations to remind them what has happened.
4. Discuss the story and see if the child can relate it to their own experience, or perhaps compare it to another story they know.
5. Give praise! Remember that small mistakes need not always be corrected.